ROMEO and JULIET

For Sarah

Other titles also available:

Macbeth
A Midsummer Night's Dream
Twelfth Night
Henry V
The Tempest

Please check website for availability in full colour

Each with an accompanying teacher's book

Visit our website at: www.shakespearecomics.com

Assistant editors: Andrew Greaves, Victoria Gemmell

Cover design: Phill Evans www.endsofinvention.biz

Pre-press production: Jane Hadlow

Editorial and proof reading services: Kathy Benzinski, Katzedit@gmail.com

Series title: Shakespeare Comic Books

Published by The Shakespeare Comic Book Company Ltd, 2010

Reprinted 2014

PEFC
PEFC/16-33-551
Printed in Poland by LF Book Services

Distributed by: NRG, 7 Knight's Park, Hussey Road, Battlefield Enterprise Park, Shrewsbury SY1 3TE

ISBN Romeo and Juliet Comic Book 978-0-9553761-4-6

British Library Cataloguing in Publication Data. A CIP catalogue record for this book is available from the British Library.

ROMEO and JULIET

in full colour, cartoon illustrated format

William Shakespeare

Edited, with a modern English translation
and illustrated by

Simon Greaves

Digitally coloured by

Phill Evans

Main characters

Escalus,
Prince of Verona

Lady
Montague — Lord
Montague

Lord
Capulet — Lady
Capulet

Romeo,
the Montagues' son

Juliet,
the Capulets' daughter

Benvolio,
Romeo's cousin

Mercutio,
a relative of
the Prince
and Romeo's
best friend

Count Paris,
a relative of
the Prince.
He wants to
marry Juliet

Tybalt,
Juliet's cousin

Friar Lawrence,
a friend to Romeo and Juliet

The nurse,
Juliet's friend

Prologue

o households, both alike in dignity,
fair Verona, where we lay our scene,
om ancient grudge break to new mutiny
here civil blood makes civil hands unclean.
om forth the fatal loins of these two foes
pair of star-crossed lovers take their life;
nose misadventured piteous overthrows
oth with their death bury their parents' strife.
e fearful passage of their death-marked
ove,
d the continuance of their parents' rage,
nich, but their children's end, naught could
emove,
now the two hours' traffic of our stage;
ne which if you with patient ears attend,
nat here shall miss, our toil shall strive to
nend.

This play is set in Verona, Italy. An old quarrel between two rich and powerful families has just started up again and many people have been hurt.

Each of these families has a child. The two children fall in love. It's only with the death of these ill-fated lovers that the quarrel is ended.

The children's love affair and the hatred between their two families – which only the lovers' death could end – is the story of the play.

So if you pay attention, you can learn about anything I've missed out here, later on.

Act 1 Scene 1

Two Capulet servants are walking in Verona.

he Capulets insult two Montague servants.

o you quarrel, sir?
e you looking for a
ht?

Quarrel, sir? No, sir.
A fight? No.

But if you do, sir, I am for you. I serve as good a man as you.
Well, if you are, I'll fight you. My master's as good as yours.

You lie.
You're lying.

fight breaks out. Benvolio arrives and tries to stop it.

raw, if you be men.
raw your swords, if you're not cowards.

Part, fools! Put up your swords. You know not what you do.
Break it up, you fools! Put your swords away. You don't know what you're doing.

Tybalt arrives.

What, art thou drawn among these heartless hinds?
Turn thee, Benvolio; look upon thy death.

Are you fighting with this scum? Turn and face your death, Benvolio.

I do but keep the peace. Put up thy sword,
Or manage it to part these men with me.

I'm only trying to keep the peace. Put your sword away – or else use it to help stop this fight.

What, drawn, and talk of peace? I hate the word
As I hate hell, all Montagues, and thee.
Have at thee, coward!

Are you talking of peace with your sword out? I hate peace as much as I hate hell, all Montagues and you. Fight, you coward!

Lord and Lady Capulet arrive.

What noise is this? Give me my long sword, ho!

What's going on? Fetch me my sword!

A crutch, a crutch! Why call you for a sword?

You're too old. You need a crutch more than a sword.

My sword, I say! Old Montague is come
And flourishes his blade in spite of me.

I want my sword! Old Montague is here and he's waving his sword in my face.

The Montagues have just arrived as well.

Thou villain Capulet!
- Hold me not; let me go.

You monster, Capulet! Take your hands off me – let me get at him!

Thou shalt not stir one foot to seek a foe.

Stay right there. You're not going anywhere looking for trouble.

Rebellious subjects, enemies to peace,
Profaners of this neighbour-stained steel –
Will they not hear? What, ho!

Rioters! Hooligans! You're spilling each others'
blood! Can't they hear me? Stop!

Throw your mistempered weapons to the ground
And hear the sentence of your moved prince.
Three civil brawls, bred of an airy word
By thee, old Capulet, and Montague,
Have thrice disturbed the quiet of our streets...
If ever you disturb our streets again,
Your lives shall pay the forfeit of the peace.

Throw down your weapons and hear what I have
to say. This is the third time that a careless word
from you – old Capulet and Montague – has led to
violence in our quiet streets. If either of you disturbs
the peace again, you'll pay for it with your lives.

The prince sends everyone away. When alone, the Montagues question Benvolio.

Who set this ancient quarrel new
broach? Who stirred up this old
quarrel again?

Here were the servants of your adversary
And yours, close fighting ere I did approach.
I drew to part them. In the instant came
The fiery Tybalt...
While we were interchanging thrusts and blows,
Came more and more, and fought on part and
 part,
Till the Prince came, who parted either part.

The fight between your servants and Capulet's
had started before I got here. I drew my sword
to part them. As I did so, that hot head Tybalt
arrived. His sword was already out. As we
fought, more and more people joined in, until
the prince turned up and put a stop to it.

O where is Romeo? Saw you him
today?
Right glad I am he was not at this
fray.

Where's
Romeo?
Have you
seen him
today?
I'm glad
he wasn't
fighting
here.

Madam, an hour before the worshipped sun
Peered forth the golden windows of the east,
A troubled mind drave me to walk abroad;
Where, underneath the grove of sycamore
That westward rooteth from this city side,
So early walking did I see your son.
Towards him I made, but he was ware of me
And stole into the covert of the wood.

Having something on my mind, I was up
before dawn. I went for a walk and saw
Romeo walking near a sycamore wood
on the western side of the city. I moved
towards him, but he spotted me and hid in
the trees.

Many a morning hath he there been seen,
With tears augmenting the fresh morning's dew,
Adding to clouds more clouds with his deep sighs;
But all so soon as the all-cheering sun
Should in the farthest east begin to draw
The shady curtains from Aurora's bed,
Away from light steals home my heavy son
And private in his chamber pens himself,
Shuts up his windows, locks fair daylight out,
And makes himself an artificial night.
Black and portentous must this humour prove
Unless good counsel may the cause remove.

He's been seen there many mornings, crying and sighing. But as soon as the sun's up, my son hurries home and locks himself in his room. He shutters his windows to keep the daylight out and lives in a world of darkness. His unhappy mood is sure to cause trouble, unless we're able to talk him out of it.

My noble uncle, do you know the cause? Do you know what's causing it?

I neither know it nor can
  learn of him...
Could we but learn from
  whence his sorrows grow,
We would as willingly give
  cure as know.

I don't know – and he won't tell me. If only we knew what was depressing him, we'd do all we could to help sort things out.

See, where he comes.
So please you step
  aside;
I'll know his grievance
  or be much denied.

Here he comes. Please leave us alone – I'll find out what's wrong with him, if it's at all possible.

Montague and his wife hurry off as Romeo arrives.

Good morrow, cousin...
What sadness lengthens
Romeo's hours?

Good morning, Romeo.
  What problem's making the hours drag by so slowly?

Not having that which having, makes them short. Not having something to make them pass quickly.

love? Are you in love?

ut of her favour where I am in ove.

I'm in love, but I'm not loved back.

Alas that love, so gentle in his view,
Should be so tyrannous and rough in proof!

It's too bad that love seems so gentle, but turns out to be so cruel and hard.

Alas that love, whose view is muffled still,
Should without eyes see pathways to his will!
Where shall we dine? O me, what fray was here?
Yet tell me not, for I have heard it all.
Here's much to do with hate, but more with love.
Why then, O brawling love, O loving hate,
O anything, of nothing first create!
O heavy lightness, serious vanity,
Misshapen chaos of well-seeming forms,
Feather of lead, bright smoke, cold fire, sick health,
Still-waking sleep, that is not what it is!
This love feel I, that feel no love in this.
Dost thou not laugh?

It's too bad that love is blind and can't see where it's aiming. But what fight was going on here? No, don't tell me, I know already – there was hatred in the fight but also a simple love of fighting. It's all upside down – people who hate, love their quarrels, but I am hated by the girl I love.

Everything has become its opposite – feathers seem as heavy as lead, fire is cold, sickness is the same as health, being asleep's like being awake. Nothing is how it should be any more. I love, yet I'm not loved back! Doesn't that make you laugh?

o, coz, I rather weep.

o, I'd rather cry.

ood heart, at what? Why?

At thy good heart's oppression.

Because you're so unhappy.

5

Why such is love's transgression.
Griefs of mine own lie heavy in my breast,
Which thou wilt propogate, to have it pressed
With more of thine. This love that thou hast shown
Doth add more grief to too much of mine own.

That's how cruel love can be. I'm heavy with sadness, but now you're sad because I'm sad and I'm sad because you're sad. I thank you for your concern, but it's only making things worse.

Love is a smoke made with the fume of sighs;
Being purged, a fire sparkling in lovers' eyes;
Being vexed, a sea nourished with lovers' tears.
What is it else? A madness most discreet.
A choking gall, and a preserving sweet.

Love is a thick smoke made from a lover's sighs – but when the smoke clears, it's the fire burning in a lover's eyes. When love can't have its way, it becomes a sea of tears. What else is love like? It's a secret madness, a bitter pill, a delicious sweet.

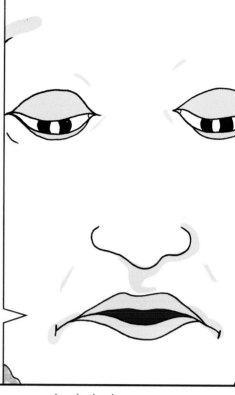

Tell me, in sadness, who is that you love?

Seriously, who is it that you love?

In sadness, cousin, I do love a woman...
She'll not be hit
With Cupid's arrow. She has Dian's wit,
And in strong proof of chastity well arme[d]
From Love's weak childish bow she lives uncharmed.

Seriously then, I'm in love with a woman but she refuses to fall in love. She's cleve[r] and strong-willed and won't let herself fa[ll] for anyone.

Then she hath sworn that she will still live chaste?...
Be ruled by me; forget to think of her. You mean she'll never give herself to anyone? Then take my advice. Don't think about her.

O, teach me how I shoul[d] forget to thi[nk]

Tell me how I can stop thinking abou[t] her.

By giving liberty unto thine eyes.
Examine other beauties.

Let your eyes wander. Look at other beauties.

Show me a mistress that is passing fair:
What doth her beauty serve but as a note
Where I may read who passed that passing fai[r]
Farewell. Thou canst not teach me to forget.

Show me any beautiful woman and all her beauty will do is remind me that the woman I love – Rosaline – is even mor[e] beautiful. Goodbye. You'll neve[r] help me forget her.

Act 1 Scene 2

Capulet is with Paris, a young man who wants to marry Juliet.

But Montague is bound as well as I,
penalty alike; and 'tis not hard, I think,
r men so old as we to keep the
peace.

ontague and I
ve both been
ven the same
arning. I don't
ink it should be
o hard for men
old as ourselves
keep the peace.

Of honourable reckoning are you both.
And pity 'tis you lived at odds so long.
But now, my lord, what say you to my suit?

You're both
respected men.
It's a shame this
quarrel has gone
on for so long.
But now, what
about my request
to marry your
daughter?

ut saying o'er what I have said before:
y child is yet a stranger in the world,
he hath not seen the change of fourteen years;
et two more summers wither in their pride
re we may think her ripe to be a bride.

I'll repeat what I told you before.
She's only fourteen and very
inexperienced. It will be another
two years before she's ready to
think about marriage.

ounger than she are
happy mothers made.

Younger girls than Juliet have become happy mothers.

nd too soon marred are those so early made.
arth hath swallowed all my hopes but she;
he is the hopeful lady of my earth.
ut woo her, gentle Paris, get her heart;
y will to her consent is but a part.
nd she agreed, within her scope of choice,
e my consent and fair according voice.

hose that grow up too quickly are the first to
row old. My other children are dead. Juliet's
e only one I have left and all my hopes lie
her.
Win her heart, Paris. My agreement is only a
art of it. It's up to her. As long as her choice is
omeone suitable, that's good enough for me.

Capulet invites Paris to a party he's holding that evening. Then he gives a servant a list of the other people he wants to attend.

Meeting Romeo and Benvolio in the street, he asks them to read the list for him – and it turns out Rosaline has been invited. In thanks for their help, the servant invites them to the party too.

My master is th[e] great rich Capu[let] and if you be n[ot] of the house of Montagues, I pr[ay] come and crush [a] cup of wine.

My master is the great rich Capulet and as long as you're not Montagues, please come an[d] have a drink.

At this same ancient feast of Capulet's
Sups the fair Rosaline whom thou so loves,
With all the admired beauties of Verona.
Go thither, and with unattainted eye
Compare her face with some that I shall show,
And I will make thee think thy swan a crow.

Rosaline, the woman you love, is going to be at Capulet's party, along with all the most beautiful women in Verona. Go to the part[y] with open eyes and I'll show you some girls who'll make Rosaline look like an old crow.

One fairer than my love?
The all-seeing sun ne'er
    saw her match since first
    the world begun.

Someone more beautiful than my Rosaline? The su[n] never looked down on anyone more lovely since the dawn of time.

Tut, you saw her fair, none else being by.
Herself poised with herself in either eye:
But in that crystal scales let there be weighed
Your lady's love against some other maid
That I will show you shining at this feast,
And she shall scant show well that now
    seems best.

You only thought her beautiful because there was no-one else nearby to compare her with. Once you've compared Rosaline with the brilliant girl I'll show you at the party, you won't think the one you thought best of all worth anything.

I'll go along, no such sight to be
    shown,
But to rejoice in splendour of
    mine own.

I'll go along, no[t] to see what you have on show, bu[t] to enjoy my own love's beauty.

Lady Capulet is keen to find out what Juliet thinks about marriage to Paris.

[Te]ll me, daughter Juliet,
[H]ow stands your
[di]spositions to
[be] married?

[Te]ll me, Juliet,
[wh]at do you
[fe]el about
[m]arriage?

It is an honour that I dream not of.
I haven't thought about it.

[W]ell, think of marriage now. Younger than
[y]ou,
[h]ere in Verona, ladies of esteem,
[a]re made already mothers. By my count,
[I w]as your mother much upon these years
[th]at you are now a maid. Thus then in brief:
[th]e valiant Paris seeks you for his love.

[W]ell think about getting married, now. Many
[we]ll brought up girls in Verona are already
[m]others – and they're younger than you as
[we]ll. I gave birth to you when I was about
[yo]ur age. Anyway, in short, Paris has asked
[to] marry you.

He's a flower; in faith, a very flower. He's the pick of the bunch!

[Th]is night you shall behold him at our feast.
[R]ead o'er the volume of young Paris' face.
[An]d find delight writ there with beauty's pen...
[Sp]eak briefly, can you like of Paris' love?

You can have a good look at him at
the party tonight. You'll see he's a
very handsome man. Do you think
you could love him?

I'll look to like, if looking
    liking move;
But no more deep will I
    endart mine eye
Than your consent gives
    strength to make it fly.

If I like what I see,
perhaps I could. But I
won't let things go further
than you would want.

Go, girl, seek happy
    nights to happy days.

Off with you now. May
happy days be followed
by even happier nights.

Act 1 Scene 4

Come, knock and enter; and no sooner in
But every man betake him to his legs.

Right, we're here! As soon as we're inside, let's get dancing!

A torch for me! Let wantons of light heart
Tickle the senseless rushes with their heels...
I'll be a candleholder and look on;
The game was ne'er so fair, and I am done.

I'll just hold a torch. Fools can dance around if they want. I'll just stand about holding a candle and watch what's going on. Dancing's not something I've ever enjoyed much anyway, and I'm feeling down.

We mean well in going to this masque,
But 'tis no wit to go.

I know it's only a bit of fun going to this party, but I feel it's not wise to go.

Why, may one ask?

Why do you say that?

I dreamt a dream tonight.

I had a dream last night.

O, then I see Queen Mab hath been with you.
She is the fairies' midwife, and she comes
In shape no bigger than an agate stone
On the forefinger of an alderman,
Drawn with a team of little atomies
Over men's noses as they lie asleep...
Her waggoner, a small grey-coated gnat,
Not half so big as a round little worm
Pricked from the lazy finger of a maid;
And in this state she gallops night by night
Through lovers' brains, and then they dream of love.

Then I can see Queen Mab's visited you. She's the one who brings dreams to life. No bigger than the stone in a town councillor's ring, she's carried by a team of tiny creatures over people's noses as they sleep. Her driver is a small grey gnat, not even as big as a little worm plucked from a lazy serving girl's finger.

Driven along in this way, she charges nightly through lovers' brains – and sends them dreams of love.

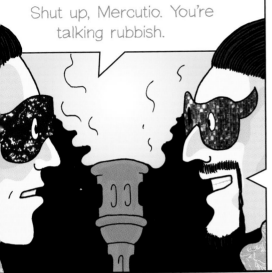

ace, peace, Mercutio, peace!
hou talk'st of nothing.

Shut up, Mercutio. You're talking rubbish.

True, I talk of dreams,
Which are the children of an idle brain,
Begot of nothing but vain fantasy;
Which is as thin of substance as the air,
And more inconstant than the wind, who woos
Even now the frozen bosom of the north
And, being angered, puffs away from thence,
Turning his side to the dew-dropping south.

True, I'm talking of dreams, which only come from brains with nothing better to think of – the products of nothing but empty thoughts. There's no more to dreams than air. They're as changeable as the wind, one moment in the freezing north, then in a fit of temper, suddenly heading to the warmer south.

his wind you talk of blows us from ourselves.

upper is done, and we shall come too late.

his wind you're talking of is blowing off course. The meal's over and we're going to miss everything.

I fear too early; for my mind misgives
Some consequence yet hanging in the stars
Shall bitterly begin his fearful date
With this night's revels and expire the term
Of a despised life, closed in my breast,
By some vile forfeit of untimely death.
But he that hath the steerage of my course
Direct my sail! On, lusty gentlemen!

I'm afraid we'll get there all too soon. I've a bad feeling this party's going to start a chain of events I can't understand or control, ending my unhappy life with an early death. But who cares? Whatever happens to me is in the hands of fate. Let's go!

Act 1 Scene 5

Capulet's party is a masque – with special dresses, masks and dances.

Welcome, gentlemen! Ladies that have their toes unplagued with corns will walk a bout with you.

Welcome, gentlemen. I'm sure any ladies whose eet aren't killing them will dance with you.

What lady's that which doth enrich the hand
Of yonder knight?

Who's the lady dancing with that man over there?

I know not, sir.

I don't know, sir.

O, she doth teach the torches to burn bright!
It seems she hangs upon the cheek of night
As a rich jewel in an Ethiop's ear –
Beauty too rich for use, for earth too dear!
So shows a snowy dove trooping with crows
As yonder lady o'er her fellows shows.

She outshines all the torches lighting up
the night. She blazes in the darkness like a
bright jewel against black skin. She's more
beautiful than anything on earth, like an angel.
Compared to all the other women, she's like a
snow white dove among a flock of crows.

The measure done, I'll watch her place of sta
And touching hers, make blessed my rude han
Did my heart love till now? Forswear it, sight!
For I ne'er saw true beauty till this night.

As soon as the dance is over, I'll watch where
she goes and touch her hand with mine. Did I
ever truly love until now?
   No never! I've never seen real beauty until
      tonight.

balt has heard Romeo's voice.

is, by his voice, should be a Montague...
hat! Dares the slave
ome hither, covered with an antic face,
fleer and scorn at our solemnity?
ow, by the stock and honour of my kin,
strike him dead I hold it not a sin.

e sounds like a Montague.
ow dare he hide his face
hind a mask and come
re to make fun of
r party? He deserves
ath on the spot.
apulet family honour
mands it.

Why, how now, kinsman?
Wherefore storm you so?

What's
up with
you, to
make
you rant
on like
this?

Uncle, this is a Montague, our foe.
A villain that is hither come in spite
To scorn at our solemnity this night.

Uncle, one of our Montague enemies
is over there. He's come to make
fun of our party.

ontent thee, gentle coz, let him alone.
bears him like a portly gentleman,
nd to say truth, Verona brags of him
be a virtuous and well-governed
youth...
herefore be patient; take no note of him,
is my will, the which if thou respect,
how a fair presence and put off these
frowns,
n ill-beseeming semblance for a feast.

alm down. Leave him alone. He looks all
ght – and to be honest, everyone in
erona says he's a well-behaved and
easant boy. Be patient. Ignore him.
s my wish that you act in a friendly
ay. And stop looking so bad
mpered – your face doesn't
in with the party mood.

It fits when such a villain is a guest.
I'll not endure him. It's fair enough
when we've someone like him as a
guest. I won't put up with him.

e shall be endured.
hat, goodman boy!
say he shall. Go to!
m I the master here,
or you?

ou will put up
ith him if I say
, you young
up! Who's
e boss here
me or you,
r goodness
ake?

Patience perforce with willful choler meeting
Makes my flesh tremble in their different greeting.
I will withdraw; but this intrusion shall,
Now seeming sweet, convert to bitt'rest gall.

Trying to control
myself when I feel
this mad gives me
the shakes.
I'll leave now. You
may think it's fine,
having a Montague
push his way in, but
it will end in trouble.

Romeo has made his way over to Juliet.

If I profane with my unworthiest hand
This holy shrine, the gentle sin is this:
My lips, two blushing pilgrims, ready stand
To smooth that rough touch with a tender
 kiss.

If it's a sin to touch this saintly hand with my rough hand, I can only say my lips are waiting to soften that rough touch with a tender kiss.

Good pilgrim, you do wrong your hand too much,
Which mannerly devotion shows in this;
For saints have hands that pilgrims' hands do touc
And palm to palm is holy palmers' kiss.

You're not being fair to your hand, friend. It's no sin for one hand to touch another – worshippers often touch the hand on the statue of a saint with their own. And hands kiss every time they're put together in prayer.

Have not saints lips, and holy
 palmers too?

Don't saints have lips as well as hands?

Ay, pilgrim, lips that they must
 use in prayer.

Oh yes. They use their lips for saying prayers.

O, then, dear saint, let lips do what hands do!
They pray; grant thou, lest faith turn to despair.

Well then, let my lips touch in prayer the way hands do. If you don't answer my prayer and let me have my wish, my faith in you will be crushed.

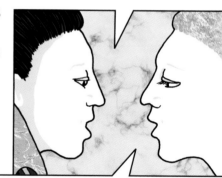

Saints do not move, though grant for prayers' sak
The lips on the statues of saints don't move, ever when they're answering a prayer.

Then move not while my
 prayer's effect I take.
Thus from my lips, by
 thine my sin is purged.

Then don't move while my prayers are answered. With this kiss, your lips take away the sin.

They kiss for the first time

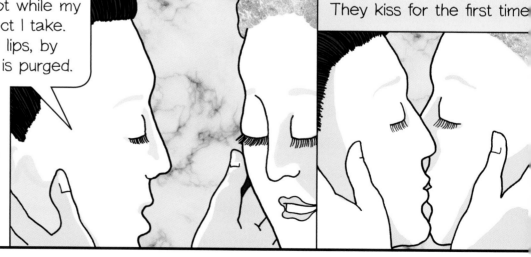

14

hen have my lips the sin that they have took.
o, the sin has passed from your lips to mine.

You kiss by the book.

You certainly know how to kiss!

n from my lips? O trespass sweetly urged!
ive me my sin again.

e passed my sin on to you? What can we do
ow? You'd better give it back to me!

Madam, your mother craves a word with you.

Your mother wants a word with you, miss.

liet goes to find her mother.

What is her mother?

Who's her mother?

Marry, bachelor, Her mother is the lady of the house. Her mother is the lady of this house.

Is she a Capulet?
O dear account! My life is my foe's debt.

A Capulet? She can't be! Then all I value in life belongs to my enemy.

omeo

arried way om he arty.

Be gone; the sport is at the best.

Let's go! The best of the party is over!

y, so I fear; the more is my unrest.

hat's what I'm afraid of. I'm full of bad feelings.

Juliet returns too late.

What is yond gentleman?...
   If he be married,
      My grave is like to be
         my wedding bed.

Who is he? If he's already married, I'll go to my grave without marrying.

is name is Romeo, and a Montague,
he only son of your great enemy.

is name is Romeo, a Montague.
e's the only son of your family's
reatest enemy.

My only love, sprung from my only hate!
Too early seen unknown, and known too late!

Prodigious birth of love it is to me
That I must love a loathed enemy.

My only true love is a hated Montague! When I first saw him, I didn't know who he was. And now I do know, it's too late! I can't believe that I've fallen in love with the son of my family's deadliest enemy.

Prologue

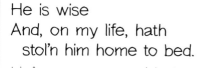

Now old desire doth in his deathbed lie,
And young affection gapes to be his heir;
That fair for which love groaned for and
   would die,
With tender Juliet matched, is now not fair.
Now Romeo is beloved and loves again,
Alike bewitched by the charm of looks.
But to his foe supposed he must complain,
And she steal love's sweet bait from fearful
   hooks.
Being held a foe, he may not have access
To breathe such vows as lovers use to swear,
And she as much in love, her means much less
To meet her new beloved anywhere.
But passion lends them power, time means,
   to meet,
Tempering extremities with extreme sweet.

Old feelings of love a
dying as a new one
born. The old love
would have given
anything for Rosaline
but now compared to
Juliet, she's nothing
special. Romeo's in love aga
and is loved in return, each
bewitched by the other's looks. B
he's fallen for one of the enemy,
and her loving him is equally
dangerous. Because he's from the
wrong family, he can't get near to
tell of his love – and although she
as much in love, it's even more
difficult for her to see him. But the
power of love gives them the
means to meet – and when they
do, it's all the sweeter.

Act 2 Scene 1

Romeo is outside the Capulets' orchard.
Benvolio and Mercutio are looking for him.

Can I go forward when my heart is here?
Turn back, dull earth, and find thy centre out.

How can I leave when all I love is here? My
heart is pulling me back towards Juliet.

He is wise
And, on my life, hath
   stol'n him home to bed.

He's seen sense. I bet
he's gone home to bed.

He ran this way and leapt this
   orchard wall.
Call, good Mercutio.

He ran this way and jumped over
the orchard wall. Give him a
shout, Mercutio!

Romeo! Humours! Madman! Passion! Lover!
Appear thou in the likeness of a sigh;
Speak but one rhyme, and I am satisfied!

Hey, Romeo – you love-struck fool. Give us a
sigh or a line of poetry to let us know you're
there.

He heareth not, he stirreth not, he moveth not.

There's no reply of any kind.

Come, he hath hid himself among these trees...
'Tis in vain
To seek him here that means not to be found.

Come on, he's hiding in the trees.
We'll never find him if he doesn't want to be found.

Act 2 Scene 2

Romeo is hiding in the Capulets' orchard.

e jests at scars, that never felt a wound.
ercutio can laugh. He's never been hurt by
ve.

ut soft! What light through yonder window
breaks?
is the east, and Juliet is the sun!
rise, fair sun, and kill the envious moon,
Who is already sick and pale with grief
hat thou her maid art far more fair than she.
e not her maid, since she is envious;
er vestal livery is but sick and green,
nd none but fools do wear it. Cast it off.

ut wait, what's that light shining from the
indow over there? It's the east, and Juliet is
he sun. Rise up and kill the moon – it's already
ck with jealousy that you are lovelier then she.
orget the feeble, sexless moon. Don't copy her.
Only fools do that.

is my lady! O, it is my love!
, that she knew she were!
he speaks, yet she says nothing. What of that?
er eye discourses; I will answer it.
am too bold; 'tis not to me she speaks.

's Juliet – the one I love – if only she knew it.
ler lips move, but make no sound. That doesn't
natter when her eyes are full of speech. But
n taking things for granted – she's not
peaking to me.

wo of the fairest stars in all the heaven,
laving some business, do entreat her eyes
o twinkle in their spheres till they return...
ee how she leans her cheek upon her hand.
, that I were a glove upon that hand,
hat I might touch that cheek!

wo busy stars have asked her eyes to shine
their place in the night sky 'til they return.
She's leaning on her hand. I wish I were a
love on it, just so I could touch her cheek.

17

Ay me!

Mmmm.

She speaks!
O, speak again, bright angel – for thou art
As glorious to this night, being o'er my head,
As is a winged messenger of heaven.

She's speaking. Say something else, you angel – it's as if a heavenly creature were floating in the sky above my head.

O Romeo, Romeo! Wherefore art thou Romeo?
Deny thy father and refuse thy name;
Or, if thou wilt not, be but sworn my love,
And I'll no longer be a Capulet.

Oh Romeo, Romeo! Why must you be who you are? Pretend you're not a Montague and change your name. If you won't – as long as you say you love me – I'll change mine from Capulet.

Shall I hear more, or shall I speak at this?

Should I wait to hear more, or should I say something in reply?

Juliet still doesn't know that Romeo is below in the orchard.

'Tis but thy name that is my enemy.
Thou art thyself, though not a Montague.
What's Montague? It is nor hand, nor foot,
Nor arm, nor face, nor any other part
Belonging to a man. O, be some other name!
What's in a name? That which we call a rose
By any other name would smell as sweet.
So Romeo would, were he not Romeo called,
Retain that dear perfection which he owes
Without that title. Romeo, doff thy name;
And for thy name, which is not part of thee,
Take all myself.

It's only a name that makes you an enemy. You'd be the same person, even if you weren't a Montague. What is a 'Montague'? It's not a hand, or foot, or arm, or any other part of the body. Just use another name.

Why do names matter? If a rose were called by any other name, it would still smell as sweetly. And Romeo would be just as perfect, even if he weren't called Romeo.

So get rid of that name – which isn't important anyway – and take me instead.

ake thee at thy word.
all me but love, and I'll be new
baptized;
enceforth I never will be Romeo.

greed! As long as you promise
love me, I'll take a new name.
om tonight I won't ever be
lled Romeo again.

liet hears Romeo's
st words.

hat man art
hou, that, thus
escreened in
ight,
o stumblest on
my counsel?

ho's that hidden
the dark,
tening to my
crets?

By a name
I know not how to tell thee who I am.
My name, dear saint, is hateful to myself,
Because it is an enemy to thee.

I don't know
how to tell
you my
name. I hate
it myself, now,
because it's
the name of
your family's
enemy.

ow camest thou hither, tell me, and wherefore?
he orchard walls are high and hard to climb,
nd the place death, considering who thou art,
any of my kinsman find thee here.

How did you get here? Why are
you here? The orchard walls are
high and hard to climb. This place
is dangerous for you – you'll be
killed if any of my family finds
you here.

ith love's light wings did I o'erperch these walls;
or stony limits cannot hold love out,
nd what love can do, that dares love attempt.
herefore thy kinsman are no stop to me.

I flew over the walls on the wings
of love. Piles of stone can't keep
love out. Love can do anything it
wants. Your relatives couldn't stop
me if they tried.

If they do see thee, they will murder thee.

If they see you, they'll kill you.

I have night's cloak to hide me from their eyes;
And but thou love me, let them find me here.
My life were better ended by their hate,
Than death prorogued, wanting of thy love.

The dark night hides me. And as long as I have your love, I don't care if they do find me here. I'd much rather die quickly, killed by them but loving you, than die slowly without your love.

By whose direction found'st thou out this place? Who told you how to find me here?

By love, that first did prompt me to inquire...
I am no pilot; yet, wert thou as far
As that vast shore washed with the farthest se
I would adventure for such merchandise.

Love forced me to come looking for you and told me how to find you, so I made my way here. I'm no sea captain, but I'd travel to the ends of the earth to be with you.

Thou knowest the mask of night is on my face,
Else would a maiden blush bepaint my cheek
For that which thou hast heard me speak tonigh

You know it's dark, otherwise I'd blush red at the thought of what you overheard me say tonight.

Fain would I dwell on form - fain, fain deny
What I have spoke; but farewell compliment!
Dost thou love me? I know thou wilt say 'Ay',
And I will take thy word. Yet, if thou swear'st,
Thou mayst prove false. At lovers' perjuries,
They say Jove laughs. O gentle Romeo,
If thou dost love, pronounce it faithfully.

I'd like to do things properly and take back wha
I said - but it's too late to worry about that nov
Do you love me? I know you'll say 'Yes' and I'll
believe you. Yet even if you promise not to, you
could still cheat on me - lovers often lie. If you
love me, please be true to me.

20

Or if thou thinkest I am too quickly won,
I'll frown and be perverse and say thee nay,
So thou wilt woo; but else, not for the world.
In truth, fair Montague, I am too fond.
And therefore thou mayst think my 'haviour light;
But trust me, gentleman, I'll prove more true
Than those that have more cunning to be strange.

If you think I'm to be had too easily, I could play
hard to get to make you chase me – but not
otherwise. In truth, I love you too much to play
games with you, and because of that you might
think I'm anybody's – but believe me, I'll be truer to
you than all those girls who pretend they're cool.

I should have been more strange, I must confess,
But that thou overheard'st, ere I was 'ware,
My true-love passion. Therefore pardon me,
And not impute this yielding to light love,
Which the dark night so discovered.

I shouldn't have spoken of my love, I admit – but
you overheard my feelings before I knew you
were there. So don't go thinking I'm easy, because
of what you only learnt by accident.

Lady, by yonder blessed moon I vow,
That tips with silver all these fruit-tree tops –

My love, I promise you by the moon
shining on these fruit trees –

O swear not by the moon,
　th'inconstant moon,
That monthly changes in
　her circled orb,
Lest that thy love prove
　likewise variable.

Don't promise by the moon
– it's always changing. You
might change too.

What shall I swear by?

What should I promise to
love you by, then?

Well, do not swear. Although I joy in thee,
I have no joy of this contract tonight.
It is too rash, too unadvised, too sudden;
Too like the lightning, which doth cease to be
Ere one can say 'It lightens'. Sweet, good night!
This bud of love, by summer's ripening breath,
May prove a beauteous flower when next we meet.

Don't promise. Although I'm in love, I'm scared it's all
too sudden – too out of control. It could be like a
lightning flash – gone before you know it.
Goodnight, my darling, let's hope our budding
summertime love grows into a beautiful flower.

O, wilt thou leave me so unsatisfied?

Is that it? Can't you give me anything more?

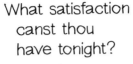

What satisfaction canst thou have tonight?

What else could I give you tonight?

Th'exchange of thy love's faithful vow for mine.

You could tell me you love me as much as I love you.

I gave thee mine before thou didst request it; And yet I would it were to give again.

I gave you my love before you even asked for it. Yet I wish I could take it back.

Wouldst thou withdraw it? For what purpose, love?

You want your love back? Why my love?

But to be frank and give it thee again. And yet I wish but for the thing I have. My bounty is as boundless as the sea, My love as deep; the more I give to thee, The more I have, for both are infinite.

Just so I could be generous and give it to you all over again, since I already have what I most long for. I give to you a love as wide and deep as an ocean. Yet the more I give to you, the more I have – there's no end to my love.

I hear some noise within... Stay but a little, I will come again.

I hear a noise. Wait there. I'll be back in a moment.

Juliet leaves.

Romeo waits.

O blessed, blessed night! I am afeard, Being in night, all this is but a dream, Too flattering-sweet to be substantial.

What a night! It's too good to be true. I'm afraid it's all a dream.

Juliet returns from talking with her nurse.

Three words, dear Romeo, and good night indeed.
If that thy bent of love be honourable,
Thy purpose marriage, send me word tomorrow,
By one that I'll procure to thee,
Where and what time thou wilt perform the rite;
And all my fortunes at thy foot I'll lay,
And follow thee my lord throughout the world.

Just a few more words – then I really have to go. If you truly love and respect me and want to marry, send me word tomorrow. Do this through someone I'll have meet you. Tell them where and at what time the marriage will take place. When it's done, all that I have to give you is yours and I'll follow you to the end of the world.

A thousand times goodnight!

A thousand times goodnight!

Juliet goes inside, leaving Romeo alone.

...thousand times the worse, to want thy light!
...ove goes toward love as schoolboys from their books;
...ut love from love, toward school with heavy looks.

...n a thousand times worse off without ...ou... Love always speeds towards ...ve, but needs to be dragged from it.

Juliet returns one last time. They agree to make further plans through her messenger, whom Romeo will meet at nine o'clock the next morning.

'Tis almost morning. I would have thee gone –
And yet no farther than a wanton's bird,
That lets it hop a little from his hand,
Like a poor prisoner in his twisted gyves,
And with a silken thread plucks it back again,
So loving-jealous of his liberty.

It's almost morning. I want you to go – but not too far. I feel like a spoilt child teasing a pet bird on a silk cord, letting it fly off a little way but then tugging it back, not wanting it lose it.

...would I were thy bird.

I wish I were your pet bird.

Sweet, so would I.
Yet I should kill thee with much cherishing.
Good night, good night!
  Parting is such sweet sorrow
That I shall say good night till it be morrow.

So do I - but I'd pet you to death.
  Goodnight, goodnight! Your leaving is so
sad yet so sweet, I could carry on saying
goodnight until tomorrow comes.

Sleep dwell upon thine eyes, peace in
  thy breast!
Would I were sleep and peace, so
  sweet to rest!

Let sleep come to your eyes and
peace settle on your breast. I'd love
to be in their place, so to be sleeping
with you.

Act 2 Scene 3

Romeo leaves Juliet and goes to see his friend, Friar Lawrence, for help.

ood morrow, father!

ood morning, Father!

Benedicite!
What early tongue so sweet saluteth me?
Young son, it argues a distempered head
So soon to bid good morrow to thy bed.

Good heavens! Who's that, so early in the morning? I'd guess you must have something on your mind, to have left your bed at this hour, young man.

Thou art uproused with some distemp'rature;
Or if not so, then here I hit it right –
Our Romeo hath not been in bed tonight.

You must have something on your mind, or if not, I'd bet you haven't even been to bed.

hat last is true.
The sweeter rest was mine.

ou're right. I found omething better than leep.

God pardon sin!
Wast thou with Rosaline?

God forgive you! Were you with Rosaline?

Vith Rosaline, my ghostly father? No.
have forgot that name, and that name's woe.

Vith Rosaline, holy father? No.
ve forgotten her and all the ain she put me through.

That's my good son! But where hast thou been then?

Good for you! But where have you been then?

Then plainly know my heart's dear love is set
On the fair daughter of rich Capulet;
As mine on hers, so hers is set on mine;
And all combined, save what thou must combine
By holy marriage. When, and where, and how
We met, we wooed, and made exchange of vow,
I'll tell thee as we pass; but this I pray,
That thou consent to marry us today.

Then let me tell you straight that my heart's love is set on Capulet's beautiful daughter. I love her and she loves me. We're completely agreed about everything, only we're not married – and we'd like you to see to that. I'll tell you how we met and fell in love and decided to marry, later. But I must ask that you agree to marry us today.

What a change is here!
Is Rosaline, whom thou didst love so dear,
So soon forsaken?...
Lo, here upon thy cheek the stain doth sit
Of an old tear that is not washed off yet.

What a sudde[n] change! Have yo[u] so quickly forgotte[n] all about Rosalin[e] who used to b[e] the love of you[r] life? Look, yo[u] haven't eve[n] washed the la[st] tears of old lov[e] from your chee[k.]

I pray thee chide me not. Her I love now
Doth grace for grace and love for love allow.
The other did not so.

Please don't be angry with me. My new love is as mad about me as I am about her. That wasn't the case before.

O, she knew well
Thy love did read by rote, that could not spell.
But come, young waverer, come go with me.
In one respect I'll thy assistant be;
For this alliance may so happy prove
To turn your households' rancour to pure love.

That's because Rosaline knew you weren't really serious. But come with me, my changeable young friend – I'll help you for one good reason. That's because the happiness of your marriage may help bring peace between your two warring families, turning hatred to love.

O, let us hence!
 I stand on
 sudden haste.

Let's be off then – as quickly as possible!

Wisely and slow[ly]
 they stumble
 that run fast.

Take your time People who go too fast, often trip up.

Mercutio and Benvolio are out looking for Romeo.

Where the devil should this Romeo be? Came he not home tonight?

Where's Romeo? Didn't he go home last night?

Not to his father's. I spoke with his man.

He didn't go to his father's house, I asked his servant.

Why, that same pale hard-hearted wench, that Rosaline, torments him so that he will sure run mad.

That awful girl Rosaline will send him out of his mind.

Here comes Romeo! Here comes Romeo!

Here's Romeo, now! Here's Romeo!

Good morrow to you both.

Hi, there!

Now art thou sociable, now art thou Romeo.

That's more friendly. You're like the old Romeo again.

Juliet's nurse arrives, looking for Romeo.

Can any of you tell me where I may find the young Romeo?

Can any of you tell me where to find a young man called Romeo?

Romeo introduces himself. He tells the nurse his plans.

Bid her devise
Some means to come
  to shrift this afternoon;
And there she shall at
  Friar Lawrence's cell,
Be shrived and married.

Ask Juliet to find a way to get to Friar Lawrence's this afternoon. There she can go to confession and be married.

And stay, good nurse, behind the abbey wall.
Within this hour my man shall be with thee,
And bring thee cords made like a tackled stair,
Which to the high top-gallant of my joy
Must be my convoy in the secret night.
Farewell! Be trusty, and I'll quit thy pains.

Good nurse, you must now wait behind the abbey wall. Within an hour, my servant will meet you there. He'll bring a rope ladder with him to help me climb in secret up to Juliet's room tonight. Goodbye. Do things right and I'll see you're well paid for your troubles.

Juliet's in the orchard. She can't wait for her nurse to return with news from Rome

The clock struck nine when I did send the nurse;
In half an hour she promised to return.
Perchance she cannot meet him. That's not so
O, she is lame!

It was nine when I sent the nurse. She said she'd return by half past. Maybe she couldn't find him. No, that's not it. She's so slow!

Had she affections and warm youthful blood,
She would be as swift in motion as a ball;
My words would bandy her to my sweet love
And his to me.
But old folks, many feign as they were dead
Unwieldy, slow, heavy and pale as lead.

If she were young and in love, she'd be as quick as a ball. My words to Romeo and his to me would speed between us. But some old people might as well be dead – they're so bumbling, slow, heavy and grey.

The nurse arrives at last.

O God, she comes! O honey nurse, what news?

She's here! Sweet nurse – what's the news?

Have you got leave to go to shrift today?

Have you permission to go to confession, today?

I have.

Yes.

Then hie you hence to Friar Lawrence's cell;
There stays a husband to make you a wife.
Now comes the wanton blood up in your cheeks.

Then get along to Friar Lawrence's. You'll find a husband there waiting to take you for his wife. I can see you're blushing!

Hie you to church. I must another way,
To fetch a ladder, by the which your love
Must climb a bird's nest soon when it is dark.
I am the drudge, and toil in your delight,
But you shall bear the burden soon at night.

You go to church. I'm off to collect a ladder. It's the one your lover will need to climb up to your nest after dark. I'm always doing the dirty work to make you happy – but tonight you'll have to do it for yourself.

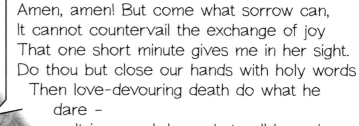

o smile the heavens upon this
holy act,
hat after-hours with sorrow chide
us not!
et's
ray this
arriage
so
appy
at
othing
appens
ter to
ake us
egret it.

Amen, amen! But come what sorrow can,
It cannot countervail the exchange of joy
That one short minute gives me in her sight.
Do thou but close our hands with holy words
Then love-devouring death do what he
dare –
It is enough I may but call her mine.

Yes, yes! But whatever
unhappiness follows, it can never
take away the joy I have in
seeing her for only a moment.
Once we're married,
love-destroying death can do
what it likes – it's enough that
I can call her mine.

These violent delights have violent ends
And in their triumph die, like fire and powder,
Which, as they kiss, consume...
Therefore love moderately: long love doth so.

Such violent pleasures end badly, blowing up
in your face.
Don't overdo things. Love lasts longest when
it's treated with care.

liet arrives to be married.

h Juliet, if the measure of
thy joy
e heaped like mine, and
that thy skill be more
blazon it, then sweeten
with thy breath
his neighbour air, and let
rich music's tongue
nfold the imagined
happiness that both
eceive in either by this
dear encounter.

h Juliet, if you're as
appy as I am, and you
an put the feeling into
etter words than me,
escribe the perfect
appiness each of us
nds in the other at this
eeting.

Conceit, more rich in matter than in words,
Brags of his substance, not of ornament.
They are but beggars that can count their worth;
But my true love is grown to such excess
I cannot sum up sum of half my wealth.

The power
of what's real
doesn't need
to be padded
out with empty
words.
Those who
can count their
wealth can't
have very much
– but my love
is so vast I
couldn't count
half of it.

They marry.

29

Act 3 Scene 1

It's early evening. Out looking for Rome[o], Mercutio and Benvolio meet Tybalt.

I pray thee, good Mercutio, let's retire;
The day is hot, the Capels are abroad,
And if we meet, we shall not 'scape a brawl,
For now, these hot days, is the mad blood
   stirring...
By my head, here comes the Capulets.

Come on, Mercutio, let's go home.
It's hot. The Capulets are about.
If we run into them, there's bound
to be a fight. The heat is driving
everyone crazy.
   Oh, oh, here they come.

By my heel, I care not.
I couldn't care less.

Follow me close, for I will speak to them.
Gentlemen, good e'en. A word with one of you[.]
Keep close behind me. I'll speak to them.
   Hi, there! I want a word with one of you!

Still upset with Romeo, Tybalt demands to know where he is. Tempers rise. Benvolio[
]tries to calm things down.

We talk here in the public haunt of men.
Either withdraw unto some private place,
Or reason coldly of your grievances,
Or else depart. Here all eyes gaze on us.

Look, everyone can see us here.
Either find somewhere private to settle
things or calm down. If not, move
   on. Everyone's looking at us.

Men's eyes were made to look, and let them gaze.
I will not budge for no man's pleasure, I.
Eyes were made for looking. Let them stare. I'm not
moving for anyone.

Well, peace be with you, sir.
   Here comes my man.
That's OK by me. Here's the
man I'm after.

omeo arrives.

omeo, the love I bear thee can afford
better term than this: thou art a villain.

omeo. Here's what I think of you: you're no better than dirt.

Tybalt, the reason that I have to love thee
Doth much excuse the appertaining rage
To such a greeting. Villain am I none.
Therefore farewell. I see thou knowest me not.

Tybalt, the good reason I have to be friends with you allows me to ignore such a greeting. I'm not a piece of dirt.
Goodbye.
I can see you know nothing about me.

by, this shall not excuse the injuries
nat thou hast done me; therefore turn and draw.

That doesn't take away the harm you've done me. Turn and fight!

do protest I never injured thee,
ut love thee better than thou canst devise
ll thou shalt know the reason of my love;
nd so, good Capulet, which name I tender
s dearly as mine own, be satisfied.

I've never done you wrong, and love you more than you could imagine – at least until you find out the reason.
Friend Capulet, your name is as precious to me as my own, believe me.

calm, dishonourable, vile submission!...
ybalt, you ratcatcher, will you walk?

hat sick-making weakness! Tybalt, you nimal, will you step over here?

Good King of Cats, nothing but one of your nine lives. Nothing, you wild cat, except one of your nine lives.

What wouldst thou have with me?

What do you want with me?

I am for you.   I'll have you.

Tybalt and Mercutio fight.

Gentle Mercutio, put thy rapier up. Stop fighting, Mercutio.

Trying to stop the fight, Romeo steps in front of Mercutio. Tybalt stabs at him under Romeo's arm, then runs off.

I am hurt.
A plague o' both your houses! I am sped.
Is he gone and hath nothing?

I'm hurt. Damn the hatred between your families. I'm done for. Has he got away unhurt?

Courage, man. The hurt cannot be much.

Pull yourself together. You can't be badly hurt.

'Tis enough, 'twill serve... A plague o' both your houses!. Why the devil came you between us? I was hurt under your arm.

It's bad enough. Damn both your families. Why did you get in the way? I was hurt under your arm.

I thought all for the best. I was only trying to help.

This gentleman, the prince's near ally,
My very friend, hath got his mortal hurt
In my behalf – my reputation stained
With Tybalt's slander – Tybalt, that an ho
Hath been my cousin. O sweet Juliet,
Thy beauty hath made me effeminate
And in my temper soften'd valour's steel!

Mercutio, the prince's close relation and m best friend is dying because he took my side against Tybalt, who'd abused me – Tybalt, who's only been my cousin for an hour. Oh, sweet Juliet, your beauty has made me soft and girlish and taken all the fight out of m

Help me into some house, Benvolio,
Or I shall faint. A plague o' both your houses!
They have made worms' meat of me.

Help me into a house, Benvolio, or I'll faint. Damn all Montagues and Capulets – I'm done for because of your families.

Benvolio returns. He tells Romeo that Mercutio is dead.

This day's black fate on moe days doth depend;
This but begins the woe others must end.

This terrible day is only the start - worse things will follow from it.

Here comes the furious Tybalt back again.

Here comes Tybalt raging back again.

Alive in triumph, and Mercutio slain?
Away to heaven respective lenity,
And fire-eyed fury be my conduct now!
Now, Tybalt, take the 'villain' back again
That late thou gavest me; for Mercutio's soul
Is but a little way above our heads,
Staying for thine to keep him company.
Either thou or I, or both, must go with him.

Tybalt's alive and boasting what he's done
While Mercutio's dying? No more being
reasonable - from this moment, let red-hot
anger be my guide.
Now, Tybalt - take back the 'dirt' you
called me earlier. Mercutio's soul is waiting
just above our heads for you. Either one or
both of us will have to join him.

Thou wretched boy, that didst consort him here,
Shalt with him hence.   You came here with him,
you baby, you can leave with him.

This shall
determine that.   My sword will decide about that.

They fight. Tybalt is killed.

Romeo, away, be gone!
The citizens are up, and Tybalt slain.
Stand not amazed. The Prince will doom
  thee death
If thou art taken. Hence, be gone, away!
Run for it, Romeo! Tybalt's dead and
people are everywhere. Don't just stand
there staring - run! The prince will have
you killed if you're caught.

O, I am fortune's fool! Bad luck always
follows me, wherever I go, whatever I do

Romeo runs off. The prince arrives
with the Montagues and Capulets.

Where are the vile beginners of this
  fray? Where are the thugs who
    started this fight?

O noble Prince, I can discover all
The unlucky manage of this fatal brawl.
There lies the man, slain by young Rome
That slew thy kinsman, brave Mercutio.
I can tell you everything - how things
turned bad and ended in bloodshed. Ther
lies the man Romeo killed, who himself ha
killed your relative, Mercutio.

He is a kinsman to the Montague;
Affection makes him false, he speaks not
  true...
I beg for justice, which thou, Prince, must
  give.
Romeo slew Tybalt; Romeo must not live.
He's lying. He's related to Romeo and
that's made him twist the truth - I beg
for justice from you, Prince. Romeo killed
Tybalt, so you must have Romeo killed.

Romeo slew him; he slew
  Mercutio.
Who now the price of his
  dear blood doth owe?
Romeo killed Tybalt for
killing Mercutio. Who's
going to pay the price
for those deaths?

Not Romeo, Prince; he was Mercutio's friend;
His fault concludes but what the law should end,
The life of Tybalt.

Not Romeo, Princ
He was Mercutio's
friend. What he
did was wrong, bu
Tybalt deserved to
die anyway.

And for that offence
Immediately we do exile him hence...
Let Romeo hence in haste,
Else, when he is found, that hour is his las
For having done what he did, Romeo shal
be exiled - sent away. He must leave as
quickly as he can. Otherwise, if he's found
here, he'll be put to death on the spot.

Act 3 Scene 2

Juliet is waiting in the orchard.

Come, night! Come, Romeo! Come, thou day in night...
Give me my Romeo; and, when I shall die,
Take him and cut him out in little stars,
And he will make the face of heaven so fine
That all the world will be in love with night
And pay no worship to the garish sun.

I can't wait for the night to come. I can't wait for
Romeo to come. He makes the night seem as bright
as day. Just give me Romeo, and when I'm dead, he
can be cut into little stars. He'll shine so beautifully
in heaven that the whole world will fall in love with
night and forget the show-off sun.

O, I have bought the mansion of a love,
But not possessed it; and though I am sold,
Not yet enjoyed. So tedious is this day
As is the night before some festival
To an impatient child that hath new robes
And may not wear them.

Oh, I have bought a gorgeous house of love, but
not moved into it – and although someone's bought
me with their love, I haven't yet been carried away.
Today's as long as the day before a special treat
when a child has been given smart new clothes
to wear, but isn't allowed to put them on.

Juliet's nurse arrives with the rope ladder. She tells Juliet of the fight. Juliet can't take it in.

Is Romeo slaughtered, and is Tybalt dead?
My dearest cousin, and my dearer lord?
Then, dreadful trumpet, sound the general
   doom!
For who is living, if those two are gone?

Are Romeo and Tybalt both dead? My much
loved cousin and much more loved husband?
Then let the trumpets sound the end of the
world! Who's truly alive if those two are dead?

Tybalt is gone, and Romeo banished; Romeo that killed him, he is banished.

Tybalt's dead and Romeo's been exiled. Romeo killed him and has had to run away.

O God! Did Romeo's hand shed
   Tybalt's blood?

Oh God! Did Romeo
kill Tybalt?

It did, it did!

He did!
He did!

O serpent heart, hid with a flowering face!..
Despised substance of divinest show!
Just opposite to what thou justly seem'st –
A damned saint, an honourable villain!...
Was ever book containing such vile matter
So fairly bound? O, that deceit should dwell
In such a gorgeous palace!

Who could believe such an evil heart lay behind that lovely face! – You looked like an angel, but all the time you were a devil, the exact opposite of what you seemed – a guilty saint, an honest seeming thief! Was there ever such a disgusting book with such attractive covers? I can't believe dishonesty could live inside such a beautiful body.

There's no trust,
No faith, no honesty in men;
   all perjured,
All forsworn, all naught, all
   dissemblers...
Shame come to Romeo.

You can never believe men –
they're all liars, cheats and
crooks, worth nothing.
I hope Romeo comes
to a bad end!

Blistered be thy tongue
For such a wish! He was not born to shame.

I hope your tongue burn up for saying such a thing. He was never meant to come to a bad end.

Will you speak well of him that
   killed your cousin?

Are you sticking up for the
man who killed your cousin?

Shall I speak ill of him that is my husband?
Ah, poor my lord, what tongue shall smooth thy
   name
When I, thy three-hours wife, have mangled it?
But wherefore, villain, didst thou kill my cousin?
That villain cousin would have killed my husband.

Are you asking me to speak badly about the man that's my husband? Ah, my poor love, what words can repair the damage I've done to your name – after less than three hours as your wife.
   But why did you kill my cousin? Because that foul cousin would have killed you, of course.

All this is comfort; wherefore weep I then?
Some word there was, worser than Tybalt's death
That murdered me. I would forget it fain;
But O, it presses to my memory...
'Tybalt is dead, and Romeo – banished.'

That makes things seem better, so why the tears? There was more news, even worse than Tybalt's death. I've tried to forget it, but it keeps returning – 'Tybalt is dead and Romeo exiled.'

Poor ropes, you are beguiled,
Both you and I, for Romeo is exiled.
He made you for a highway to my bed;
But I, a maid, die maiden-widowed.
Come cords; come, nurse. I'll to my wedding bed;
And death, not Romeo, take my maiden-head!

Poor ladder, we've both been cheated – Romeo has been sent away. He made you as the quickest way to my bed, but now I'll die never having known his body. Come ladder, come nurse – I'm going to my wedding bed, but death, not Romeo, will have the first pleasure of me.

[...]e to your chamber. I'll find Romeo
[...] comfort you. I wot well where he is.
[...]ark ye, your Romeo will be here at night.
[...] to him.

[...]o to your room. I'll find Romeo to [...]mfort you. I know where he's hiding. [...]e'll be with you tonight. [...]'ll go to him now.

Act 3 Scene 3

After killing Tybalt, Romeo runs to hide at Friar Lawrence's.

[...]meo, come forth; come
[...]th, thou fearful man.
[...]fliction is enamoured of
[...]hy parts,
[...]d thou art wedded to
[...]alamity.

[...]me out, Romeo, you [...] happy man. [...]me here. [...]oubles love [...]u. Disaster [...]llows you [...]verywhere.

Father, what news? What is the Prince's doom?
What sorrow craves acquaintance at my hand
That I yet know not?

What's the news? What's the prince's decision? What's the latest trouble to hit me?

[...]bring thee tidings of
[...]e Prince's doom.

[...]e news [...]f the [...]rince's [...]ecision.

What less than doomsday is the Prince's doom?

How much less bad than death is it?

Not body's death, but body's banishment.

You're not to die, but you are to be exiled.

Ha, banishment? Be merciful, say
    'death';
For exile hath more terror in his look,
Much more than death.
    Do not say banishment.

Exiled? Be kind and say 'death'.
Being sent away is much worse
        than death. Don't say
            I'm to be exiled.

O deadly sin! O rude unthankfulness!
Thy fault our law calls death, but the kind
    Prince,
Taking thy part, hath rushed aside the law,
And turned that black word 'death' to
    banishment.
This is dear mercy, and thou seest it not.

How ungrateful can you get! You shou
    have been sentenced to death fo
    what you did, but the kind princ
    has taken your side and ber
        the rules – changing you
        sentence from death t
            exile. That's re
        kindness and yo
            can't see

'Tis torture, and not mercy. Heaven is here,
Where Juliet lives; and every cat and dog
And little mouse, and every unworthy thing,
Live here in heaven and may look on her...
But Romeo may not, he is banished.
Flies may do this but I from this must fly;
They are freemen, but I am banished.
And sayest that yet that exile is not death?

It's cruelty, not kindness. Heaven is here, with
Juliet – and every cat and dog and little mouse
and the smallest slimy thing lives in heaven
because they can look at her – but not me. I'm
to be sent away. Flies can look at her, but I have
to fly off. They are free, but I'm sent away. And
you say that's not the same thing as death?

Let me dispute with thee of thy
    estate.

Let me talk over your
        situation with you.

Thou canst not speak of that thou dost not fee
Wert thou as young as I, Juliet thy love,
An hour but married, Tybalt murdered,
Doting like me, and like me banished,
Then mightst thou speak, then mightst thou tea
    thy hair,
And fall upon the ground, as I do now,
Taking the measure of an unmade grave.

You can't talk over what you don't know about
If you were as young as me, only married an
hour to your love, Juliet, as much in love as
me – with Tybalt murdered and were then sen
away, then you'd have a right to talk.
    If you knew all that, then you could tear you
hair and fall to the ground as if being sized up
for a grave, the way I am now.

38

omeo throws
nself to the
ound. The
rse arrives
find him
n the floor
tears.

O, he is even in my mistress' case,
Just in her case! O woeful sympathy!
Piteous predicament! Even so lies she,
Blubbering and weeping, weeping and blubbering.
Stand up, stand up! Stand, and you be a man.
For Juliet's sake, for her sake, rise and stand!

It's just the same with Juliet. They're both
as bad as each other. What a terrible
situation! She's lying down, crying her
eyes out, as well. Get up! Behave!
Pull yourself together
for Juliet's sake!

pakest thou of Juliet? How is it with her?
oth not she think me an old murderer,
ow I have stained the childhood of our joy
'ith blood removed but little from her own?
here is she? And how doth she?

re you talking about
liet? How is she?
oes she think I'm
sed to murdering now
'e splattered the first
ours of our love with
er cousin's blood?
Where is she? How
she?

O, she says nothing, sir, but weeps
and weeps;
And now falls on her bed, and then
starts up,
And Tybalt calls; and then on
Romeo cries,
And then down falls again.

She says nothing, just cries
and cries - throws herself
on her bed, then gets up
again. She calls out Tybalt's
name, then yours - then
throws herself down again.

omeo tries to stab himself but the nurse stops him.

s if that name,
not from the deadly level of a gun,
id murder her; as that name's
cursed hand
urdered her kinsman.
O, tell me, friar, tell me,
what vile part of this
anatomy
oth my name lodge?
Tell me, that I may sack
he hateful mansion.

s as if my name
ere shot from a gun,
urdering her the way my
and murdered Tybalt.
Tell me, friar, in what
inking part of my body
y name is to be found.
ell me so I can destroy it.

Hold thy desperate hand.
Art thou a man?...
Hast thou slain Tybalt?
Wilt thou slay thyself?

Stop that at once! Are you
a man? You've killed Tybalt.
Are you going to kill
yourself next?

What, rouse thee, man! Thy Juliet is alive,
For whose dear sake thou wast but lately dead.
There art thou happy. Tybalt would kill thee,
But thou slewest Tybalt. There art thou happy.
The law, that threatened death, becomes thy friend,
And turns it to exile. There art thou happy.
A pack of blessings light upon thy back;
Happiness courts thee in her best array;
But, like a misbehaved and sullen wench,
Thou pouts upon thy fortune and thy love.
Take heed, take heed, for such
    die miserable.
Go get thee to thy love, as was
    decreed.
Ascend her chamber, hence
    and comfort her.
But look thou stay not till
    the watch be set,
For then thou canst not
    pass to Mantua,
Where thou shalt live till
    we can find a time
To blaze your marriage,
    reconcile your friends,
Beg pardon of the Prince,
    and call thee back
With twenty hundred thousand
    times more joy
Than thou went'st forth in lamentation.

Pull yourself together, man. Juli...
for whom you were about to ...
yourself is alive and well - tha...
excellent. Tybalt would ha...
killed you, but you killed Tyb...
- that's good too. The law th...
could have put you to death is ki...
and instead only sends you into ex...
- even better. Lots of good thin...
have happened to you, but you'...
sulking like a spoilt child. Ta...
care, for people like you ...
unhappy. Go and find yo...
love as planne...
Climb up to her bedroo...
and comfort her. B...
make sure you lea...
before the guards a...
out, or you won't ...
able to get to Mantu...
Stay there until we fi...
time to tell people ...
your marriage, g...
your families to agr...
to it, and ask a pard...
from the prince. Y...
can then come back w...
all the sadness of your leavi...
turned into massive joy at your retur...

Go before, nurse. Commend me to thy lady.
And bid her hasten all the house to bed,
Which heavy sorrow makes them apt unto.
Romeo is coming.

You go on ahead, nurse. Give my
best wishes to Juliet and tell her to
hurry everyone in the house to bed
- with all in such low spirits, that
shouldn't be hard.
Tell her, Romeo is coming.

The nurse
leaves. Th...
friar tells
Romeo
again that
he must b...
out of tow...
before
sunrise,
then
Romeo
leaves.

Act 3 Scene 4

At the Capulets' house it is now very late.

ings have fallen out, sir, so unluckily
hat we have had no time to move our daughter.
ook you, she loved her kinsman Tybalt dearly,
nd so did I. Well, we were born to die.
is very late. She'll not come
down tonight.

nings have
rned out so
adly, we've
ad no time to
lk to Juliet
bout marrying
u. She loved
er cousin
balt very
uch, as did I.
Oh well, we
l have to die
me time.
t's so late,
don't think
e'll come
wn tonight.

These times of woe afford no times to woo.
Madam, good night.
   Commend me to your daughter.

This sad time isn't a good one to try to win her love. Goodnight, madam. Please give Juliet my best wishes.

I will, and know her mind early tomorrow;
Tonight she's mewed up to her heaviness.

I will. I'll find out what she thinks about the marriage tomorrow. Tonight she's too sad.

r Paris, I will make a desperate tender
f my child's love. I think she will be ruled
 all respects by me; nay, more, I doubt it not.
ife, go you to her ere you go to bed;
cquaint her here of my son Paris' love...
' Thursday let it be - o' Thursday, tell her,
he shall be married to this noble earl.
ill you be ready? Do you like this haste?

an't make any promises, Sir Paris, but I
ink I can offer you my daughter's love. I think
e'll do what I say - no, I'm sure of it. Go to
ee her on your way to bed, wife. Tell her of
aris' love for her, and on Thursday - yes, on
hursday - she'll marry him. Will you be ready,
aris? What do you say to this speed?

My lord, I would that
   Thursday were tomorrow.

I wish Thursday were tomorrow.

Well, get you gone. O' Thursday be it then.
Go you to Juliet ere you go to bed;
Prepare her, wife, against this wedding day.

That's settled then. Thursday it is. Go to Juliet on your way to bed, wife, and prepare her for her wedding day.

Act 3 Scene 5

Wilt thou be gone? It is not yet near day.
It was the nightingale, and not the lark,
That pierced the fearful hollow of thine ear.
Nightly she sings on yond pomegranate tree.
Believe me, love, it was the nightingale.

In Juliet's bedroom.

Do you have to go? It's nowhere
near daytime. It was a night bird,
not the morning lark your anxious
ear heard. She sings every night i
the fruit tree over there. Trust me
my love, it was a nightingale.

It was the lark, the herald of the morn,
No nightingale. Look, love, what envious
  streaks
Do lace the severing clouds in yonder east.
Night's candles are burnt out and jocund
  day
Stands tiptoe on the misty mountain tops.
I must be gone and live, or stay and die.

It wasn't a nightingale, it was the lark,
telling us morning has come. Look, my
love, the first unfriendly streaks of ligh
are breaking through the clouds there
in the east. The stars are gone and a
bright, new day is stretching over thos
misty mountain tops. I have to go, if I
want to live, or I can stay here and di

ond light is not daylight. I know it, I.
... is some meteor that the sun exhales
... be to thee this night a torch-bearer
... nd light thee on thy way to Mantua.
... herefore stay yet, thou need'st not to
be gone.

...hat light isn't daylight, I'm
...ure. It's a meteor flaming
...om the sun to light you
...hrough the night on your
...ay to Mantua. That
...eans you can stay.
...You don't need to go yet.

I have more care to stay than will to go.
Come, death, and welcome!
    Juliet wills it so.
How is't, my soul? Let's talk; it is not day.

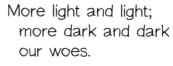

I'd much rather
stay than go.
    Come Death!
Welcome - it's
what Juliet wishes.
How are you my
love? Let's talk,
it's nowhere near
daytime.

...is, it is! Hie hence,
...be gone, away!...
..., now be gone! More
...light and light it grows.

...is, it is! You have to
...ave right now!
...Go on - it's getting
...ghter and lighter!

More light and light;
    more dark and dark
    our woes.

The lighter it gets
outside, the darker
our problems seem
to become.

...he nurse arrives.

...ur lady mother is coming
...to your chamber.
...he day is broke; be wary,
...look about.

...ur mother's
...n her way
...ere. It's
...aytime
...lready.
...ake care.
...Vatch
...ut.

Then, window, let day in, and let life out.
Then in through the window comes the day. Out
through the window goes the love of my life.

Farewell, farewell! One kiss, and I'll descend.
Goodbye. One last kiss and I'll climb down.

...?, think'st thou
...e shall ever
...eet again?

...o you think
...e'll ever
...eet again?

I doubt it not; and all these
    woes shall serve
For sweet discourses in our
    times to come.

I'm sure of it - then all these
problems will seem nothing but
amusing stories to talk over in
our future life together.

O God, I have an ill-divining soul!
Methinks I see thee, now thou art so low,
As one dead in the bottom of a tomb.
Either my eyesight fails, or thou lookest pale.

Oh God, I've a bad feeling about all this. Now you're down below, it seems as if you're dead and at the bottom of a grave. There could be something wrong with my eyes, but you look pale.

And trust me, love, in my eye so do you.
Dry sorrow drinks our blood. Adieu, adieu! Believe me, my love, so do you. Our deep sadness drains us of colour. Goodbye, goodbye.

Romeo leaves.

Juliet's mother arrives.

Why, how now, Juliet?...
Evermore weeping for your cousin's death?

What's going on, Juliet? Are you still crying about your cousin's death?

Yet let me weep for such a feeling loss.

I can't help crying over such an unhappy loss.

We will have vengeance for it, fear thou not.
Then weep no more. I'll send to one in Mantua,
Where that same banished runagate doth live,
Shall give him such an unaccustomed dram
That he shall soon keep Tybalt company;
And then I hope thou wilt be satisfied...
But now I'll tell thee joyful tidings, girl.

We'll get our own back for it, don't you worry. Stop crying. I'll send someone to Mantua, where Romeo's living and have him poisoned. He'll soon be keeping Tybalt company. That should make you feel better. But now, I've some good news for you, my girl.

And joy comes well in such a needy time.
What are they, beseech your ladyship?

We've need of good news at such a sad time as this. What is it, mother?

arry, my child, early next Thursday morn
he gallant, young, and noble gentleman,
he County Paris at St Peter's Church,
hall happily make thee there a joyful bride.

ell child, early next hursday morning, ou're to be married the handsome nd well-born aris in St Peter's hurch.

Now by Saint Peter's Church, and Peter too,
He shall not make me there a joyful bride!
I wonder at this haste, that I must wed
Ere he that should be husband comes to woo.
I pray you tell my lord and father, madam,
I will not marry yet.

By St Peter and his Church, I certainly won't be made a happy bride there. I'm astonished at this speed – that I'm to be married before my future husband's even been to see me.
Please tell my father that I won't marry yet.

apulet arrives with liet's nurse.

ow now, wife? ave you delivered to her our decree?

reetings, wife. Have ou told her our ans?

Ay, sir; but she will none, she gives you thanks.
I would the fool were married to her grave!

Yes. She says, 'Thanks,' but she won't hear of it. I wish the fool were dead.

ow? Will she none? Doth she not give us thanks?
s she not proud? Does she not count her blessed,
nworthy as she is, that we have wrought o worthy a gentleman to be her bride?

What? She won't hear of it? Isn't she pleased? Is she too good for us? Isn't she thrilled that although she's so worthless, we've found her such a fine gentleman to marry?

ot proud you have, but thankful that you have.
roud can I never be of what I hate, ut thankful even for hate that is meant love.

I'm not pleased you have, although I'm grateful. I can't be thrilled with what I hate, but I thank you for arranging the marriage all the same – even though I hate it – because I know you did so out of love.

Hang thee, young baggage! Disobedient wretch!
I tell thee what - get thee to church o' Thursday
Or never after look me in the face...
Thursday is near; lay hand on heart, advise:
And you be mine, I'll give
    you to my friend;
And you be not, hang, beg,
    starve, die in the streets.
For, by my soul, I'll ne'er
    acknowledge thee,
Nor what is mine shall
    never do thee good.

Go to hell, you little slut! Yo
disobedient worm! I'm tellir
you this - you can get to churc
on Thursday or else never se
me again. Thursday is comir
soon. Think about it. If yo
agree to what I want, I'll marr
you to my friend. If not, yo
can starve and die in th
streets, for on my lif
I'll cut you off ar
no-one here w
ever lift a finge
to help yo

Capulet leaves.

Is there no pity sitting in the clouds
That sees into the bottom of my grief?
O sweet my mother, cast me not away!
Delay this marriage for a month, a week;
Or if you do not, make the bridal bed
In that dim monument where Tybalt lies.

Isn't there any pity in
heaven that sees how
desperate I am? Oh,
dear mother, don't give
up on me. Put the
marriage off for a
month, even a week. Or
if you won't, get ready
to see me lying in the
same tomb as Tybalt.

Talk not to me, for I'll not speak a word
Do as thou wilt, for I have done with
thee. Don't talk to me. I'm not on your
side. You can do what you like, because
I've finished with you.

Lady Capulet leave.

O God! - O nurse, how shall this be prevented?...
What say'st thou? Hast thou not a word of joy?
Some comfort, nurse.

Oh, God!
Nurse, how
can I stop
this? What
do you
suggest?
Have you
anything
good to
say? Give
me some
comfort,
nurse.

I think it best you married wit
    the County.
O, he's a lovely gentleman!
Romeo's a dishclout to him...
I think you are happy in this
    second match,
For it excels your first...
Your first is dead - or 'twere
    as good he were.

I think you should marry Paris
He's a lovely gentleman.
Romeo's a wet rag compare
to him. I think you'd be happy
in the marriage. It's even
better than your first. Your fir
husband's dead - or at least
he's as good as dead.

Well, thou hast comforted me marvellous
   much.
Go in; and tell my lady I am gone,
Having displeased my father, to
   Lawrence's cell,
To make confession and to be absolved.

Well thanks – you've really cheered me
up. Go and tell my mother that having
upset my father, I've gone to Friar
Lawrence's to ask to be forgiven.

Marry, I will;
  and this is
  wisely done.

I will. You're
doing just the
right thing.

The nurse
leaves.

Ancient damnation! O most wicked fiend!
Is it more sin to wish me thus forsworn,
Or to dispraise my lord with that same tongue
Which she hath praised him with above compare
So many thousand times? Go counsellor!
Thou and my bosom henceforth shall be twain.
I'll to the friar to know his remedy.
If all else fail, myself have power to die.

What a nasty old woman! What an evil witch! Is it
worse to want me to go back on my word, or to
abuse my love with the same tongue she's used to
praise him to the skies a thousand times before?
That's it! I've had enough of her. I'll never ask for
her help again. I'm off to the friar to find out what
he suggests. If nothing else, I can always kill myself.

Act 4 Scene 1

Juliet finds Paris already visiting Friar
Lawrence.

Are you at leisure, holy father, now,
Or shall I come to you at evening mass?

Are you free now, father, or shall I come
to see you at church this evening?

My leisure serves me, pensive daughter,
  now.
My lord, we must entreat the time alone.

I've time to see you now, my sad child.
My lord, I must ask you to leave us alone.

God shield I should
  disturb devotion!
Juliet, on Thursday
  early will I rouse ye.

God forbid I should
get in the way of
your religious duties.
  I'll wake you early
on Thursday
morning, Juliet.

Paris leaves.

O Juliet, I already know thy grief;
It strains me past the compass of my wits.
I hear thou must, and nothing may prorogue it,
On Thursday next be married to this County.

I already know your trouble, Juliet. It's been driving
me mad. I hear you have to marry Paris next
Thursday and that nothing can put it off.

Juliet suddenly takes out a knife.

Tell me not, friar, that thou hearest of this,
Unless thou tell me how I may prevent it.
If, in thy wisdom, thou canst give no help,
Do thou but call my resolution wise
And with this knife I'll help it presently...
    I long to die
If what thou speak'st speak not of remedy.

Don't tell me you already know about it
unless you can tell me how to stop it. If with
all your cleverness you're not able to help,
just agree it's the best thing to do and I'll stab
myself straightaway with this knife. I'd rather
be dead if you can't come up with anything.

Hold, daughter. I do spy a kind of hope,
Which craves as desperate an execution
As that is desperate which we would prevent...
If thou darest, I'll give thee remedy.

Wait, child. I've an idea. It will be almost as
terrible to carry out as the trap we're
trying to avoid, but if you're brave enough,
I'll give you the answer.

O, bid me leap, rather than marry Paris,
From off the battlements of any tower...
Or hide me nightly in a charnel house,
O'ercovered quite with dead men's
    rattling bones,
With reeky shanks and yellow
    chapless skulls;
Or bid me go into a
new-made grave
And hide me with a dead man
    in his shroud –
Things that, to hear them told,
    have made me tremble –
And I will do it without fear
    or doubt
To live an unstained wife to
    my sweet love.

Tell me to leap from the top of a tower
or hide me every night in a house of
death, covered over with dead
men's rattling bones, their
stinking legs and yellow
jawless skulls. Or tell me
to jump into a newly dug
grave with a dead man
in his blanket - things
that used to make me
shake just to hear
them talked about
– and I'd do
without fear or
question, as
long as I can
stay my love's
pure wife.

old, then. Go home, be merry, give consent
o marry Paris. Wednesday is tomorrow.
omorrow night look that thou lie alone;
et not the nurse lie with thee in thy chamber.
ake thou this vial, being then in bed,
nd this distilled liquor drink thou off;
hen presently through all thy veins shall run
 cold and drowsy humour...
ach part, deprived of supple
government,
hall, stiff and stark and cold,
appear like death;
nd in this borrowed likeness
of shrunk death
hou shalt continue
two-and-forty hours
nd then awake as from
a pleasant sleep.
ow, when the bridegroom
in the morning comes
o rouse thee from thy bed,
there art thou - dead.
hen, as the manner of the country is,
 thy best robes uncovered on the bier,
hou shalt be borne to that same
ancient vault
here all the kindred of the Capulets lie.
 the meantime, against thou shalt awake,
hall Romeo by my letters know our drift;
nd hither shall he come; and he and I
ill watch thy waking, and that very night
hall Romeo bear thee hence to Mantua.
nd this shall free thee from this
present shame
 no inconstant toy nor womanish fear
bate thy valour in the acting it.

Right, then. Go home, look cheerful
and agree to marry Paris.
Tomorrow is Wednesday. Make sure
you're alone tomorrow night – don't
let your nurse sleep in the room.
When you're in bed, take this little
bottle and drink what's in it. Shortly
after that you'll feel cold and
sleepy. You won't be able
to move and your body
will become as stiff and
cold as death. You'll
seem to be dead for
forty two hours, and
then wake as from
a pleasant sleep.
Now, when the
bridegroom comes
to wake you in the
morning, he'll find
you dead. Then, as
always happens here,
you'll be dressed in
your best clothes and
carried in an open
coffin to the underground
tomb where all the Capulets are
buried. Before you wake, I will write
to Romeo to let him know what's
happening and he'll come back –
then together we'll wait for you to
wake up. That very night Romeo
will take you back to Mantua. So,
as long as you keep to the plan,
and don't lose your nerve, you'll be
out of this difficult situation.

liet agrees. Friar
awrence gives her the
ink, promising again to
rite to Romeo to tell
m of the plan.

ord give me strength,
 and strength shall help
afford.
arewell, dear father.

od give me the strength
need. Goodbye, father.

Act 4 Scene 2

The Capulets are busy preparing Juliet['s] wedding party when she returns home[.]

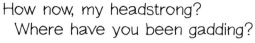

How now, my headstrong?
 Where have you been gadding?

Now then, my naughty girl. Where have you been flying off to?

Where I have learnt me to repent the sin
 Of disobedient opposition
 To you and your behests[.]
 Henceforward I am ev[er]
 ruled by you.

I've been where I've learnt how wrong I was to disobey you and you[r] commands. From now on, I'll do everything you say.

Send for the County. Go tell him of this.
I'll have this knot knit up tomorrow morning...
Now, afore God, this reverend holy friar,
All our whole city is much bound to him...
My heart is wondrous light,
Since this same wayward girl is so reclaimed.

Go and give Paris the good news! Tell him about this. I'll have the wedding tomorrow morning. By God, the whole city owes Friar Lawrence many thanks. I feel wonderful now my problem daughter has come to her sense[s].

Act 4 Scene 3

Juliet is in her room talking to the nurs[e] when Lady Capulet arrives.

Ay, those attires are best; but gentle Nurse,
I pray thee leave me to myself tonight;
For I have need of many orisions
To move the heavens to smile upon my state,
Which, thou well knowest, is cross and full of sin.

Yes, that's the best outfit, but please let me be alone tonight. I've need of many prayers asking heaven to look kindly on my situation – which is a bad one, as you know only too well.

What, are you busy, ho? Need you my help?

Are you busy? Do you need any help?

o, madam; we have culled such necessaries
s are behoveful for our state tomorrow.
o please you, let me now be left alone,
nd let the nurse this night sit up with you;
or I am sure you have your hands full all
this so sudden business.

o, mother. We've sorted everything we need
r tomorrow. Please leave me now – and let
e nurse sit up with you. You must have your
ands full with the speed of all this.

Lady Capulet and the nurse leave.

arewell! God knows when we shall meet again.
have a faint cold fear thrills through my veins
hat almost freezes up the heat of life.
call them back again to comfort me;
urse! – What should she do here?
y dismal scene I needs
must act alone.
ome vial.
'hat if this mixture do
not work at all?
hall I be married then
tomorrow morning?
o, no! This shall prevent it…
'hat if it be a poison which the friar
ubtly have minist'red to have me dead,
est in this marriage he should be dishonoured
ecause he married me before to Romeo?
ear it is; and yet methinks it should not,
or he hath still been tried a holy man.
ow if, when I am laid into the tomb,
wake before the time that Romeo
ome to redeem me? There's
a fearful point!
hall I not then be stifled in the vault,
whose foul mouth no healthsome
air breathes in,
nd there die strangled ere my
Romeo comes?
r, if I live, is it not very like
his horrible conceit of death
and night,
ogether with the terror of the place –
s in a vault, an ancient receptable
'here for this many hundred years the bones
f all my buried ancestors are packed;
'here bloody Tybalt, yet but green in earth,
es fest'ring in his shroud; where, as they say,
t some hours in the night spirits resort.

Goodbye. God knows when we'll meet again. A faint, cold fear rushes through me, freezing the life out of me. I'll call them back to comfort me – Nurse! But what's the point? I have to do this dreadful thing alone. Come, bottle. But what if it doesn't work? Would I have to marry after all? No, my dagger would put a stop to that. But what if it's a poison the friar's given to kill me – to stop himself being blamed for having married me to Romeo? I'm afraid that's the case, but then again, he's believed to be a good man. Yet what if they put me in the tomb and I wake before Romeo comes to find me? That's too horrible! Won't I be suffocated by the foul air, before Romeo reaches me? And even if I live, won't I be driven mad by the terror of the place – where my ancestors' bones have been kept for hundreds of years – where the newly dead Tybalt is rotting in his death blanket? People say there are ghosts there!

51

Alack, alack, is it not like that I,
So early waking - what with the loathsome
  smells,
And shrieks like mandrakes torn out of the
  earth,
That living mortals, hearing them, run mad -
O, if I wake, shall I not be distraught,
Environed with all these hideous fears,
And madly play with my forefathers' joints,
And pluck the mangled Tybalt from his shroud,
And in this rage, with some great kinsman's
  bone
As with a club dash out my desperate brains?
O, look! Methinks I see my cousin's ghost
Seeking out Romeo, that did spit his body
Upon a rapier's point. Stay, Tybalt, stay!
Romeo, Romeo, Romeo, I drink to thee.

Oh, no. Isn't it likely that I'll wake early
- what with the foul smells and the yells of
mad things torn from the earth which send
ordinary people crazy? Or if I wake, won't
I go mad, surrounded by all those frightening
things and wildly play with my ancestors'
skeletons? Perhaps I'll pull the broken Tybalt
from his sheet and in this crazy state bash
my brains out with a famous relative's bone.
  But look! I think I see Tybalt's ghost
searching for Romeo, the one whose sword
point put an end to him. Stop, Tybalt, stop!
Romeo, Romeo, Romeo, I'm drinking this for
you!

Juliet drinks the liquid and falls
behind the bed curtains.

Act 4 Scene 4

Capulet is up early, making final preparation
He tells the nurse to wake Juliet.

Come, stir, stir, stir! The second cock hath crowed
The curfew bell hath rung, 'tis three o'clock.
Look to the baked meats, good Angelica;
Spare not for cost...
Go waken Juliet; go and trim her up.
I'll go and chat with Paris. Hie, make haste,
Make haste! The bridegroom he is come already.
Make haste, I say.

Wake up, wake, wake! The cock's crowed twice
and the bell's rung. It's three o'clock! Make sure
there are enough meat pies, Angelica - don't worr
about the cost. Go and wake Juliet and get her
ready. I'll go and chat with Paris. Hurry up, hurry u
The bridegroom's here already. Hurry up, I say.

Act 4 Scene 5

The nurse has found Juliet's body. Everyone rushes to the bedroom.

he's dead, deceased. She's dead!
he's dead, she's died! She's dead!

Ha! Let me see her. Out, alas! she's cold.
Let me see her. She's cold. She's gone!

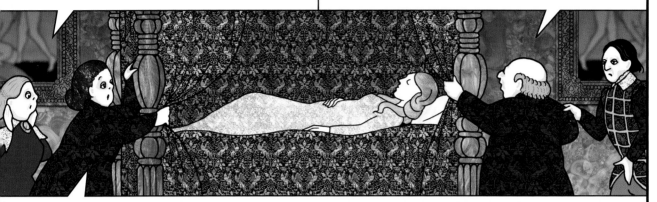

ack the day, she's dead, she's dead! Disaster! She's dead, she's dead!

ome, is the bride ready to go to church?
the bride ready to go to church?

Ready to go, but never to return.
She's ready to go, but not to return.

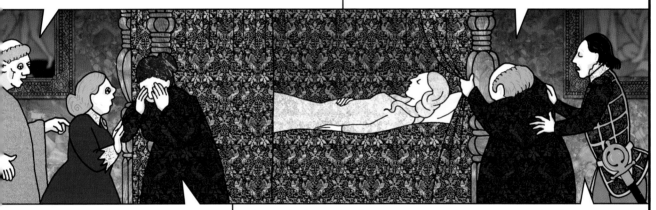

ccursed, unhappy, wretched,
hateful day!
vil, awful, miserable, hateful
ay.

Have I thought long to see this morning's face,
And doth it give me such a sight as this?
I've been looking forward to this morning so much.
I never dreamed it would be like this.

lack, my child is dead,
nd with my child my joys are
buried. My child is dead. With
her goes all the happiness in
my life.

Peace, ho, for shame! Confusion's cure lives not
In these confusions. Heaven and yourself
Had part in this fair maid – now heaven hath all,
And all the better is it for the maid...
Everyone prepare
To follow this fair corse unto her grave.
The heavens do low'r upon you for some ill;
Move them no more by crossing their high will.

For goodness sake, be quiet! You won't change
anything with all this noise. Everyone get ready
to follow this lovely dead child to her grave.
 Heaven is obviously angry with you for
something you've done wrong – don't make it
worse by complaining about what's happened.

53

Act 5 Scene 1

Romeo is in Mantua. He is waiting for his servant to bring news of Juliet from Veron

If I may trust the flattering truth of sleep,
My dreams presage some joyful news at hand.
My bosom's lord sits lightly in his throne,
And all this day an unaccustomed spirit
Lifts me above the ground with cheerful thought
I dreamt my lady came and found me dead
(Strange dream that gives a dead man leave to
    think!)
And breathed such life with kisses in my lips,
That I revived and was an emperor.
Ah me! How sweet is love itself possessed,
When but love's shadows are so rich in joy!

If it's possible to believe in dreams, good news is on its way. My heart is filled with so much love, I've been in high spirits all day. I feel as if I'm floating on air. I dreamed that Juliet came and found me dead – a strange dream where the dead are still able to think – then her kisses brought me back to life and I felt like a king.
How wonderful it is to be in love, when even dreams of love are so amazing.

Romeo's servant, Balthazar, arrives.

How now, Balthazar?
Dost thou not bring me letters from the
    friar?
How doth my lady? Is my father well?
How fares my Juliet? That I ask again,
For nothing can be ill if she be well.

Hi, Balthazar. Have you any letters from the friar? How's Juliet? Is my father well? How's Juliet? I'm asking again because nothing could be wrong as long as she's OK.

Then she is well, and nothing can be ill.
Her body sleeps in Capel's monument,
And her immortal part with angels lives.
I saw her laid low in her kindred's vault
And presently took post to tell it you.

Then she's fine and nothing's wrong. Her body's at rest in the Capulet tomb and she's in heaven with the angels. I saw her being lowered into place and then came to tell you about it straight away.

Then I defy you, stars!
Thou knowest my lodging.
Get me ink and paper
And hire post horses.
I will hence tonight...
Hast thou no letters to
me from the friar?

Alright, fate – do your worst! I'm ready to fight. Balthazar, you know where I live. Get me ink and paper and hire some horses. I'm leaving tonight. Have you any letters from the friar?

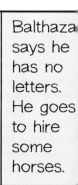

Balthaza says he has no letters. He goes to hire some horses.

Well, Juliet, I will lie with thee tonight.
Let's see for means. O mischief, thou art swift
To enter in the thoughts of desperate men!
I do remember an apothecary,
And hereabouts he dwells...
As I remember, this should be the house.

Well, Juliet, I'll be sleeping with you tonight - but
how? I've an idea - how quickly dangerous thoughts
come to people who are on the edge. There's a
drug seller nearby. This is the house, I think.

Romeo enters the shop. The
owner is very poor.

Let me have
A dram of poison, such
  soon-spending gear
As will disperse itself through
  all the veins
That the life-weary taker may
  fall dead.

Give me a bottle of poison –
something that spreads quickly
through the body, killing the
life-sick person that takes it.

Such mortal drugs I have; but Mantua's law
Is death to any he that utters them. I do
have
deadly
drugs
like
that, but
anyone
selling
them in
Mantua
would
be put
to death.

The man
is so
poor, he
at last
agrees
to sell
Romeo
the
poison.

Put this in any liquid thing you will,
And drink it off, and if you had
  the strength
Of twenty men, it would dispatch
  you straight.

Put this in any liquid and drink
it. Then, even if you had the
strength of twenty men, it would
kill you in a second.

There is thy gold - worse poison to men's souls,
Doing more murder in this loathsome world,
Than those poor compounds that thou mayst not sell.
I sell thee poison; thou hast sold me none...
Come, cordial and not poison, go with me
To Juliet's grave; for there must I use thee.

Here's your money - it's worse than poison. It does
more harm in the world than all the drugs you're not
allowed to sell. I'm giving you poison, you haven't sold
me any - it's a pleasant drink, not poison. It's coming
with me to Juliet's grave, since that's where I'm going
to use it.

Act 5 Scene 2

Friar Lawrence's messenger has returned with bad news. On his way to Mantua, Friar John had stopped in a house where people were thought to have the plague. Since nobody was allowed to leave, Friar John couldn't get out to take the letter to Romeo.

Unhappy fortune! By my brotherhood,
The letter was not nice, but full of charge,
Of dear import; and the neglecting it
May do much danger.

What a disaster! That letter was really important and the fact it didn't arrive could mean serious trouble.

Now must I to the monument alone.
Within this three hours will fair Juliet wake.
She will beshrew me much that Romeo
Hath had no notice of these accidents;
But I will write again to Mantua,
And keep her at my cell till Romeo come –
Poor living corse, closed in a dead man's tomb!

I have to get to the tomb, alone. Juliet will wake within three hours. She'll be angry that Romeo's not been told all that's happened. I'll write again to Mantua and keep Juliet here until Romeo arrives. Poor girl, buried alive among the dead

Act 5 Scene 3

Paris is in the churchyard, his servant nearby.

What cursed foot wanders this way tonight,
To cross my obsequies and true love's rite?
What, with a torch? Muffle me, night, awhile.

Who the devil's this, come to spoil my last goodbyes to the one I love? Whoever it is has a torch. I'll wait in the darkness and see.

Romeo arrives with his servant but soon sends the man away.

Give me that mattock and the wrenching iron.
Hold, take this letter. Early in the morning
See thou deliver it to my lord and father.
Give me the light.

Give me that pickaxe and iron bar. Right! Take this letter. Make sure you deliver it to my father first thing tomorrow morning.
Give me the torch.

ris
es
omeo
eaking
o
liet's
mb.

Stop thy unhallowed toil,
vile Montague!...
Condemned villain, I do
apprehend thee.
Obey, and go with me;
for thou must die.

Stop your evil
work, you hated
Montague! You're
a wanted man.
I'm arresting you.
Give yourself up
and come with
me. You must die.

nust indeed, and therefore came I hither.
ood gentle youth, tempt not a desperate man.
y hence and leave me...
t not another sin upon my head
y urging me to fury. O, be gone!
y heaven, I love thee better than myself,
or I come hither armed against myself.
ay not, be gone.

o right. That's why I came here. Don't push
e too far, friend. Leave me be. Get away
om here. Don't force me to do something I'd
gret by making me angry. I love you more
an I love myself, since I came here to kill
yself. Don't wait. Get out!

aris wants to fight. His servant
ns for help. Paris is killed.

I am slain! If thou be merciful,
pen the tomb, lay me with Juliet.

n done for! If you've any kindness,
pen the tomb and lay me beside
liet.

I'll bury thee in a triumphant grave.
A grave? O, no a lantern, slaughtered youth.
For here lies Juliet, and her beauty makes
This vault a feasting presence full of light.
Death, lie thou there, by a dead man interred.

I'll bury you in a wonderful grave. A grave?
No, it's a brilliant, shining room – for Juliet's
here and her beauty fills the whole place with
glittering light. Lie there, dead friend – one
dead man burying another.

faith, I will. Let me peruse this
face.
ercutio's kinsman, noble County
Paris!
hat I will. Let's see who it is. It's
ercutio's relative, Paris!

O my love, my wife!
Death, that hath sucked the honey
  of thy breath,
Hath had no power yet upon thy beauty.
Thou art not conquered. Beauty's
  ensign yet
Is crimson in thy lips and in
  thy cheeks,
And death's pale flag is not
  advanced there...
Why art thou yet so fair? Shall
  I believe
That unsubstantial death is amorous,
And that the lean abhorred monster keeps
Thee here in dark to be his paramour?
For fear of that I still will stay with thee
And never from this palace of dim night
Depart again. Here, here will I remain
With worms that are thy
  chambermaids. O, here
Will I set up my everlasting rest
And shake the yoke of inauspicious stars
From this world-wearied flesh. Eyes, look
  your last!
Arms, take your last embrace! And lips, O you
The doors of breath, seal with a righteous kiss
A dateless bargain to engrossing death!
Come, bitter conduct; come, unsavoury guide!
Thou desperate pilot, now at once run on
The dashing rocks thy seasick weary bark!
Here's to my love! O true apothecary,
Thy drugs are quick. Thus with a kiss I die.

Oh my love, my wife, Death has stopped your sweet breath, but has done nothing to your beauty. You haven't lost anything. Your lips and cheeks are still full of colour. The paleness of death hasn't reached you yet. How come you're still so beautiful? Is it too much to believe that Death has fallen in love with you and that the skinless, hateful beast is keeping you here in the dark to be his lover? Just in case, I'll stay with you here on this stone bed forever. I'll lie here where you have only worms to look after you. My everlasting rest begins here, at the place where I shall free myself of all my bad luck and my world-sick body. Eyes, look for the last time. Arms, take your last embrace. And lips, through which I take the breath of life, close with a kiss the contract made with an all consuming death. All right, you gruesome guide, lead me on the way to destruction. I drink to you, Juliet. Drug seller, you were right – your drugs work fast. So with a kiss, I die.

The friar arrives a second after Romeo's death. Just afterwards, Juliet wakes up.

Where is my lord?
I do remember
  well where I
  should be,
And there I am.
  Where is my
  Romeo?

Where's my husband? I know where I'm supposed to be. I'm here – but where's Romeo?

I hear some noise. Lady, come
  from that nest
Of death, contagion and
  unnatural sleep...
Stay not to question for the
  watch is coming.
Come, go, good Juliet. I dare
  no longer stay.

I hear a noise. Come away from this place of death, disease and everlasting sleep. Don't ask questions – guards are coming. Come on. I daren't stay any longer.

What's here? A cup closed in my true love's hand? Poison, I see, hath been his timeless end. O churl! Drunk all, and left no friendly drop to help me after? I will kiss thy lips. Haply some poison yet doth hang on them to make me die with a restorative. Thy lips are warm!

What's this? A bottle in my lover's hand? Poison has taken his life. You beast – you've drunk it all. There's not a drop to help me follow you. I'll kiss your lips. Perhaps there's still some poison left on them so I can drink and die. Your lips are warm.

Yea, noise?
   Then I'll be brief.
   O happy dagger!
This is thy sheath;
   there rust, and
   let me die.

There's a noise.
Then I'll be quick.
Oh, happy dagger.
You belong inside
me. Stay there till
you rust. So let
me die.

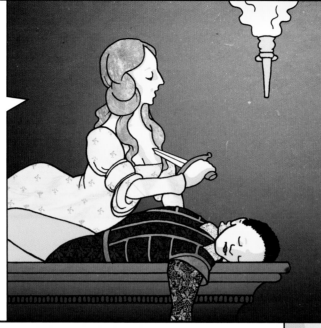

Juliet stabs herself
with Romeo's knife
just as Paris' servant
arrives with some
law officers. They
have found the friar
and Balthazar hiding
in the churchyard.
Soon after, the princ
the Capulets and
Montague arrive. The
friar and Balthazar te
the whole story. The
prince is angry at wh
he hears.

Where be these enemies? Capulet, Montague,
See what a scourge is laid upon your hate,
That heaven finds means to kill your joys with love.
And I, for winking at your discords too,
Have lost a brace of kinsmen. All are punished.

Where are those enemies, Capulet and Montague?
See how your hatred has been punished. The children
that you loved have been killed for loving one another.
I'm punished too, for not putting a stop to your hatred,
since I've lost two relatives. We've all been punished.

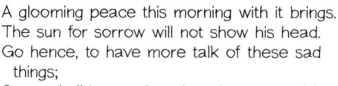

O brother Montague, give me thy han
Give my your hand, brother.

Capulet and Montague make friends.
Montague says he'll have Juliet's
statue built in gold, so she'll never be
forgotten. Capulet promises to build
one of Romeo.

A glooming peace this morning with it brings.
The sun for sorrow will not show his head.
Go hence, to have more talk of these sad
   things;
Some shall be pardoned, and some punished;
For never was a story of more woe
Than this of Juliet and her Romeo.

This dark morning brings with it an unhappy
peace. Even the sun's too sad to show its
face. Go now. Talk over these sad events.
Some people will be forgiven, others
punished. There's never been a sadder
story than this one of Romeo and Juliet.

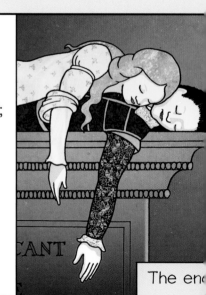

CANT

The en